Dragon's Breath Adventure

Story by Sandy Rudd

Pictures by John Gibbs

Build a Book Collective
New Namibia Books

Between Grootfontein and Tsumeb there is a farm called Harasib.

At the farm, below the ground, is the world's largest underground lake, called 'Dragon's Breath Hole.'

Some say a dragon lives there, as sometimes you can see his breath coming up from the ground in wisps of smoke.

1

Many years ago, at the village near Harasib, lived a young girl called Ndahafa. This is her story, the story of a girl who met a dragon.

Ndahafa loved to go for walks and explore the countryside. Some people said Ndahafa lived in a place with drab brown thorn bushes. But Ndahafa did not agree. She loved her village and the countryside. She liked to collect wild flowers and shining rocks.

When Ndahafa went for walks by herself, her grandmother would scold her and tell her she should not go so far, for surely the dragon would get her.

The villagers were afraid of the dragon, because sometimes they would see the smoke rising from the black, weather-worn rock. They would nod their heads and say 'Ah! the dragon is angry today.'

The day Ndahafa met the dragon was like this. She had gone for a walk and was feeling tired, so she sat down in the shade of an old thorn tree.

Suddenly, from out of the ground, came a loud noise and a large spray of hot smoke.

'AH, the Dragon!' screamed Ndahafa, and started running as fast as she could towards the village.

But in her fright Ndahafa did not see where she was going.

She tripped over a stone and fell down into the steamy darkness of the dragon's hole.

'H E E L P!' she cried and closed her eyes in fright.

Ndahafa landed on a soft sandy beach by a beautiful blue lake. Silvery bubbles sparkled up through the crystal-clear water.

High above her was the roof of the cave, shining and glistening with long hanging rocks. 'Welcome to my home,' a deep voice said behind her.

Ndahafa swung around, her heart pounding with fear. There in front of her was the most beautiful creature she had ever seen.

He was all the colours of this enchanted world. He had brilliant blue and green scales, and his wings were shining and glistening like the rocks on the roof. Best of all, he had such a kind face.

'Oh!' said Ndahafa, 'You are beautiful and friendly. How could I be afraid of you?'

The dragon opened his mouth wide and laughed and laughed. 'Ha! Ha! Ha!'

As he laughed, smoke came out of his nose and mouth. 'No one should be afraid of me – I'm a friendly dragon. Come, I'll take you to meet all the other creatures of the dragon's breath hole.'

Ndahafa climbed onto the dragon's back.

Slowly, they dived into the clear water. It felt warm and soft against her skin.

When Ndahafa saw the creatures she said happily
'Oh, I've never seen such beautiful things.'

The dragon found a piece of white rock and gave
it to Ndahafa. He told her it was from a stalactite

and she should put it with her rock collection.

'I've had such a good time,' said Ndahafa. Thank you for showing me around your home. I'll never forget you or the creatures of dragon's breath.'

It was time to go. The dragon gently bowed his head and Ndahafa carefully climbed up his scales and out of the dragon's breath hole.

When people of the village see Ndahafa playing with her rock, they ask her where she found such a fine piece. She says, in the shade of an old thorn tree.

Now, when the dragon's breath rises from the black, weather-worn rock, the villagers nod their heads and say 'Ah! the dragon is angry today.'

Ndahafa smiles and says to herself 'He's not cross.'

'He's laughing,'